STAY WITH YOUR BUDDY

Always have a buddy and be a buddy!

Rocket and his Buddy

☆ **Draw a picture of you and your buddy!** ☆

Me and my Buddy

KNOW YOUR ROAD SIGNS

Always follow traffic safety rules.

☆ In these four pictures, draw yourself being street smart with your buddy Rocket. ☆

LOOK FOR LANDMARKS

Wherever you go, notice the buildings and places around you.

Airport

Police Station

Bridge

School

Stadium

Fire Station

Hospital

City Hall

6

☆ Find and circle the landmarks in the city. ☆

☆ (Circle) 3 DIFFERENCES ☆
between the identical pictures.

1. Party Hat 2. Cupcake 3. Coffee Cup

1. Plane Backwards 2. Crown 3. Flying Saucer

7

FIND SAFE PEOPLE AND PLACES

There are people and places that are safe and others that are not safe.

☆ Help Rocket choose the safest path home. ☆

LOCATE YOUR EXITS

Always look for more than one exit.
Not all exits are doors!

☆ **Draw a line from Rocket to his two closest exits.** ☆
Some exits don't have signs.

USE YOUR VOICE

No matter where you are, you can use your powerful voice to yell for help.

HELP IS ON THE WAY

Police officers are always
ready to help you, protect you
and keep you safe.

☆ Color these pages! ☆

GET AWAY FROM DANGER

Never play with dangerous objects.

BOOK

RX

DANGER
DO NOT TOUCH

Toys

☆ Draw a line from the object to the correct box. ☆

GREAT JOB!

☆ You've earned your S.O.S. Safety Squad Badge! ☆